Odd Gardeners

INTRO TO
PHASE 5

/ue/

Level 4+
Blue+

BookLife

Helpful Hints for Reading at Home

The graphemes (written letters) and phonemes (units of sound) used throughout this series are aligned with Letters and Sounds. This offers a consistent approach to learning whether reading at home or in the classroom.

THIS BLUE+ BOOK BAND SERVES AS AN INTRODUCTION TO PHASE 5. EACH BOOK IN THIS BAND USES ALL PHONEMES LEARNED UP TO PHASE 4, WHILE INTRODUCING ONE PHASE 5 PHONEME. HERE IS A LIST OF PHONEMES FOR THIS PHASE, WITH THE NEW PHASE 5 PHONEME. AN EXAMPLE OF THE PRONUNCIATION CAN BE FOUND IN BRACKETS.

Phase 3			
j (jug)	v (van)	w (wet)	x (fox)
y (yellow)	z (zoo)	zz (buzz)	qu (quick)
ch (chip)	sh (shop)	th (thin/then)	ng (ring)
ai (rain)	ee (feet)	igh (night)	oa (boat)
oo (boot/look)	ar (farm)	or (for)	ur (hurt)
ow (cow)	oi (coin)	ear (dear)	air (fair)
ure (sure)	er (corner)		

New Phase 5 Phoneme	ue (blue, glued, clue)

HERE ARE SOME WORDS WHICH YOUR CHILD MAY FIND TRICKY.

Phase 4 Tricky Words			
said	were	have	there
like	little	so	one
do	when	some	out
come	what		

TOP TIPS FOR HELPING YOUR CHILD TO READ:

- Allow children time to break down unfamiliar words into units of sound and then encourage children to string these sounds together to create the word.

- Encourage your child to point out any focus phonics when they are used.

- Read through the book more than once to grow confidence.

- Ask simple questions about the text to assess understanding.

- Encourage children to use illustrations as prompts.

INTRO TO PHASE 5

/ue/

This book introduces the phoneme /ue/ and is a Blue+ Level 4+ book band.

Odd Gardeners

Written by
John Wood

Illustrated by
Kris Jones

The town gardening contest has begun!
All of the gardens look stunning.

But there are lots of odd gardeners in the contest this year.

This is Elmer. He has blue sunflowers. The gardeners have never seen a blue sunflower!

This is Winifred. She has glued clocks on her hands.

This is Sanam. She has snails in her pockets. There are snails in her garden too.

This is Baz. Baz has tools to dig down,
but no tools to get back up.

This is Drue. He has a garden of mushrooms. There are no flowers at all!

This is Sue. Sue needs to do some gardening, but she is sleeping like a starfish.

This is… the gardeners do not have a clue! There is so much hair.

This is Prue. Her garden looks good and she has no mud on her at all!

"Prue's garden is too good," sobs Winifred. "It cannot be true!"

Elmer comes to Prue's garden.
"Do not step on my garden!" yells Prue.

Elmer gets near, but then there is a growl. Then there is a groan.

There is a deep shudder. The garden shivers and shifts.

Then Prue's garden… stands up!
"It cannot be true," murmurs Baz from
the deep.

It is a big monster with a garden on its back!

The roots of the flowers are stuck to the monster's back like glue.

"No no no," wails Prue. "It took years to train this monster to sit still."

Sanam yells in shock. The monster gets a fright and runs off.

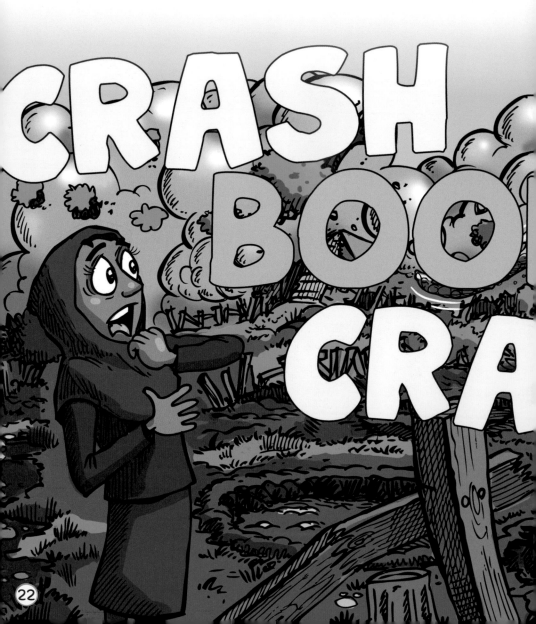

"Look out!" yells Winifred. The monster stomps up and down.

It stomps on tools. It kicks a shed.
"My mushrooms!" groans Drue.

It slips into a pond. It poos in a pot.
"My blue sunflowers!" moans Elmer.

It flattens flowers. It steps on Sue.
Sue is not hurt. Sue is still asleep.

It trips. It slips. It skids out of the town!
"My monster!" howls Prue.

It is the end of the contest. And the winner is... no one.

What a mess. There will be no gardening contest next year.

Odd Gardeners

1) What is glued to Winifred's hands?

2) What colour is Elmer's sunflower?

3) What did Drue grow in his garden?
   a) Flowers that smelled like poo
   b) Pink potatoes
   c) Mushrooms

4) What would you plant in your garden?

5) Do you think Prue was cheating? Was it fair on the other gardeners?

©2022 **BookLife Publishing Ltd.**
King's Lynn, Norfolk PE30 4LS

ISBN 978-1-80155-173-1

Odd Gardeners
Written by John Wood
Illustrated by Kris Jones

An Introduction to BookLife Readers...

Our Readers have been specifically created in line with the London Institute of Education's approach to book banding and are phonetically decodable and ordered to support each phase of the Letters and Sounds document.

Each book has been created to provide the best possible reading and learning experience. Our aim is to share our love of books with children, providing both emerging readers and prolific page-turners with beautiful books that are guaranteed to provoke interest and learning, regardless of ability.

BOOK BAND GRADED using the Institute of Education's approach to levelling.

PHONETICALLY DECODABLE supporting each phase of Letters and Sounds.

EXERCISES AND QUESTIONS to offer reinforcement and to ascertain comprehension.

BEAUTIFULLY ILLUSTRATED to inspire and provoke engagement, providing a variety of styles for the reader to enjoy whilst reading through the series.

AUTHOR INSIGHT:
JOHN WOOD

An incredibly creative and talented author, John Wood has written about 60 books for BookLife Publishing. Born in Warwickshire, he graduated with a BA in English Literature and English Language from De Montfort University. During his studies, he learned about literature, styles of language, linguistic relativism, and psycholinguistics, which is the study of the effects of language on the brain. Thanks to his learnings, John successfully uses words that captivate and resonate with children and that will be sure to make them retain information. His stories are entertaining, memorable, and extremely fun to read.

INTRO TO
PHASE 5
/ue/

This book introduces the phoneme /ue/ and is a Blue+ Level 4+ book band.